Spiritual Encouragement for Your Fitne

MW00630100

THE
BODY
TITHE
DEVOTIONAL

STUDY GUIDE

MATTHEW PRYOR

Printed in the United States of America
First Printing, 2016

ISBN 978-0-9970385-2-1

Sophros, LLC
9700 Park Plaza Avenue
Suite 203
Louisville, KY 40241

www.bodytithe.com

Contents

Author Acknowledgments

"I would like to thank Matthew and Kim Pryor for approaching me about this project and having faith in my abilities even when I had doubts.

Many thanks to my closest friends who have helped me dive into the Word and challenged me spiritually to get to know Jesus on a personal level.

I could not have done this without the support and encouragement of my family. Your love and encouragement during my weight loss years meant so much. Alex, CJ, Dani, Jesse and Luke: thank you for pushing me to be a better Mom, Mother-in-law and Nanna. To my amazing husband John, thanks for being my biggest supporter and encourager. Your love through thick and thin has been amazing. I love you forever.

Last, but not least thank you to my Heavenly Father who is the author of Life."

—Lorie Weires

"Acknowledgments are much more difficult than one might expect, but here it goes.

First, I want to thank God for giving me the ability to run. It was while I was on a run that the idea for this study guide and working with Lorie came to me. I give Him all the credit for that.

Second, I want to thank everyone that participated in our online groups and the lovely ladies that were part of our first pilot group. Thank you for being our Guinea pigs and for being so faithful and encouraging. Your input was invaluable.

Third, I want to thank Lorie for taking this project on. What a blessing you are and I am forever grateful for your friendship. You are gifted in many ways, but especially at loving people well.

And last, but certainly not least, I want to thank my family. To my sweet kiddos for the grace they constantly extend to me. To my hubby for persevering through the writing of his first book and then believing in and trusting Lorie and I with it. I'm amazed by you."

—Kim Pryor

"First, I want to thank the online Body Tithe Challenge Groups, as well as the Study Guide pilot group. Your interest and feedback helped lay the foundation for what we pray will be a life-changing study for all who participate.

I want to thank Lorie for your willingness to join us in creating this study. You are uniquely talented, gracious, and a joy. We could not have done this without you.

I also want to thank my entire family for their continued support, especially Kim. Thank you for dreaming with me and then working tirelessly on bringing that dream to fruition. You are a priceless treasure.

Finally, I want to thank my Heavenly Father. To see how lives are being changed because of what He has done through *The Body Tithe Devotional*, I'm thrilled, humbled, and eternally grateful. What a privilege to serve Him in this way!"

—Matthew Pryor

The Body Tithe Devotional Study

And so it begins: Day 1 of 90. Are you excited? We are looking forward to seeing how God meets each of us right where we are. We are eager to see how He demonstrates His love and grace to us. We are ready to see how He draws us to Himself, aligning our hearts with His through the grace of His son Jesus.

We have each been placed in this study for a specific purpose. As we persevere through these 90 days together, it's going to be amazing to watch that purpose unfold.

How to Use this Study Guide:

This study guide accompanies *The Body Tithe Devotional: Spiritual Encouragement for Your Fitness Journey*. For each of the daily readings from *The Body Tithe Devotional*, you will have corresponding questions to answer in the study guide. For example, after reading the Week 1 Preview in *The Body Tithe Devotional*, go to *The Body Tithe Devotional Study* Week 1 and answer the question posed for Week 1 Preview.

Each day, make a note of three important aspects of this study:

1. **Daily Spiritual Exercise**

   Each week you will have a new Daily Spiritual Exercise to practice. ***Please do not skip these exercises.*** They are imperative to helping you achieve your spiritual and physical goals! If you follow the study guide and practice the Daily Spiritual Exercises, you will develop habits that can last a lifetime.

2. **Today's Victory**

   There are going to be many emotional ups and downs throughout the 90 days. You have to be on guard! Avoid letting the results of your fitness efforts dictate your motivation and emotions. The goal is to **maximize** the ups and **minimize** the downs! Focus on the long-term results and life changes you are establishing.

   You will do this by recording a victory you experience each day throughout your journey. This can range from "I read the devotional and did the study questions today when I wanted to watch TV instead" to "I chose to pass up the sweet tea and opted for water instead" to "I exercised today." Again, the goal is to acknowledge the daily victories God gives you *throughout* the journey, not just at the *completion* of the journey.

3. Scripture Writing

At the end of each day's lesson, you will see a section titled "Scripture Writing." The Bible verses listed correlate to the topic for that day. They are an additional source of encouragement.

Take a moment to write out the designated Bible verses for that day. The goals are to develop the invaluable daily discipline of reading and writing out God's Word. This portion of the study reinforces that habit, so do not skip it!

With that in mind, are you ready? Let's get started by completing the Mission Statement.

The Body Tithe Devotional Study Mission Statement

You have made the decision to get healthy and allow God into this part of your life. You are excited and ready to go. This is what we call the "*Fire Phase*." Capture this excitement and focus as you put your personal mission statement into words.

"And we know that in all things God works for the good of those who love him, who have been called according to his purpose."
—Romans 8:28

Why are you setting out on this journey? What do you want to accomplish? Identifying the "Why" is equally, if not more important than the "What." If we don't know why we are doing what we are doing, it's too easy to become distracted or discouraged.

By defining the "Why," we can get at the heart of the issue. This usually reveals an emotional or spiritual stumbling block that needs to be addressed.

On the other hand, the "Why" sometimes includes someone else as part of the equation. You will find that when you have "outward focused" goals, goals that benefit others and not just yourself, you're more likely to achieve them. **So do not ignore the "Why."**

Take a moment to detail "why" you are embarking on this journey. Then list "what" you want to accomplish in these three areas of physical fitness: exercise, nutrition and sleep.

Why are you going on this journey?

_____

_____

_____

_____

_____

_____

_____

_____

_____

_____

As it relates to your physical fitness, what do you hope to accomplish with your exercise?

_____

_____

_____

_____

_____

_____

_____

What are you hoping to gain by improving how and what you eat?

_____

_____

_____

_____

_____

_____

_____

What outcome do you hope to achieve by improving your sleeping habits?

Defining success before you start will give you benchmarks from which you can measure your progress. With that in mind, what will a successful 90-day journey look like for you?

Week 1 Preview | *Names for Jesus*

How are you going to put into practice the Daily Spiritual Exercise of "praying without ceasing" this week?

_____

_____

_____

_____

_____

_____

_____

_____

_____

_____

_____

_____

_____

_____

_____

_____

_____

_____

_____

_____

Week 1 Preview | *Names for Jesus*

Week 1 Day 1 | *Names for Jesus: Cornerstone*

Daily Spiritual Exercise: Pray without ceasing.

What if your primary fitness goal were to honor God with the stewardship of your body, regardless of any physical results you realize? How would making God your cornerstone affect your ability to tackle the struggles and pitfalls you will face on this journey?

_____

_____

_____

_____

_____

_____

Today's VICTORY

_____

_____

_____

_____

_____

Scripture Writing: Psalm 5:2–3

_____

_____

_____

_____

_____

_____

_____

Week 1 Day 2 | *Names for Jesus: Bread of Life*

Daily Spiritual Exercise: Pray without ceasing.

What would happen if you consistently fed your spirit with the Bread of Life rather than settling for "food that spoils"?

Would praying without ceasing change what you do when you find yourself losing focus or motivation?

What about when you are mindlessly reaching for food or watching TV?

_____

_____

_____

_____

_____

Today's VICTORY

_____

_____

_____

_____

_____

Scripture Writing: Ephesians 6:18

_____

_____

_____

_____

_____

Week 1 Day 3 | *Names for Jesus: Radiance of God's Glory*

Daily Spiritual Exercise: Pray without ceasing.

Inspiration or reflection? What's the difference to you? Inspiring others can be a good thing, but under what conditions? If someone does call you an "inspiration," what will you do to give the Glory back to Him?

_____

_____

_____

_____

_____

Today's VICTORY

_____

_____

_____

_____

_____

Scripture Writing: Matthew 26:41

_____

_____

_____

_____

_____

_____

_____

Week 1 Day 4 | *Names for Jesus: Rabbi*

Daily Spiritual Exercise: Pray without ceasing.

How has Jesus been your Rabbi? What is He teaching you right now? How can you specifically apply that to your fitness for the remainder of this week and beyond? Remember that Jesus is empathetic to your troubles and wants to listen to you. Pour out to Him what has been causing you to struggle. Next, "be still and know that He is God." Then pause and listen. Finally, give Him glory for what He teaches you.

REFLECT

On Day 4 of each week, we will reflect on how the week has been going and we'll plan ahead for the next few days.

So, how is your week going so far? Are you reading daily? Are you "praying without ceasing"? If not, why? What's holding you back?

How can you move forward in His grace today?

"Commit to the Lord whatever you do, and he will establish your plans."
—Proverbs 16:3

Today's VICTORY

Scripture Writing: Colossians 4:2

Week 1 Day 5 | *Names for Jesus: The Shepherd and The Lamb*

Daily Spiritual Exercise: Pray without ceasing.

Page 27 says, "He is both the doctor and the medicine." As the sheep of His pasture, we go to our Good Shepherd for what we need. He can fuel our fitness, shape our focus and strengthen our resolve. What do you need from your Good Shepherd?

_____

_____

_____

_____

_____

Today's VICTORY

_____

_____

_____

_____

_____

Scripture Writing: 1 Thessalonians 5:16–18

_____

_____

_____

_____

_____

_____

Week 1 Day 6 | *Names for Jesus: The Author*

Daily Spiritual Exercise: Pray without ceasing.

Based on today's reading about Jesus as The Author, are you willing to put down the pen? Will you entrust the plot of your life to a much better writer? If so, what does that look like for you exactly? If not, why not? What is holding you back?

_____

_____

_____

_____

_____

_____

Today's VICTORY

_____

_____

_____

_____

_____

Scripture Writing: James 5:16

_____

_____

_____

_____

_____

Week 1 Day 7 | *Names for Jesus: Morning Star*

Daily Spiritual Exercise: Pray without ceasing.

Are you a morning person? What are your thoughts on Jesus as the Morning Star? Does it help to think of Him as your compass, both physically and spiritually, every morning?

Today's VICTORY

Scripture Writing: Romans 8:26–28

Weekly Recap

Use the space below to comment on anything that struck you as you were reading. Were you especially encouraged by something? Convicted? Confused? Motivated? The list could go on and on. Write down today's date and what God is revealing to you. Then, come back and read it in a year or two or 10 to see how God has interceded.

Week 2 Preview | *Old Testament Heroes*

Read Job 38–41. What verses in the reading stood out to you on the "Bigness" of God? Do you find yourself putting limits on God? How can the reminder that *nothing is beyond his abilities* help you on your journey?

_____

_____

_____

_____

_____

_____

_____

_____

_____

_____

_____

_____

_____

_____

_____

_____

_____

_____

_____

Week 2 Day 1 | *Old Testament Heroes: David*

Daily Spiritual Exercise: Meditate on an attribute of God.

Which attribute did you choose and why?

_____

_____

_____

_____

David was intentional in choosing his five stones. How might being more intentional on this journey help you? Do you need to plan a week ahead of time, or on a daily basis? Will this plan focus on nutrition, exercise, and sleep? In the space below, schedule a time to make a plan for your fitness. Be sure to pray for wisdom and direction for what that plan should look like. Then ask yourself, "Am I serious about *intentionally* following the plan?"

_____

_____

_____

_____

Today's VICTORY

_____

_____

_____

_____

Scripture Writing: Psalm 145:8–9

_____

_____

_____

_____

Week 2 Day 2 | *Old Testament Heroes: Job*

Daily Spiritual Exercise: Meditate on an attribute of God.

Which attribute did you choose and why?

_____

_____

_____

_____

When Job's friends started mischaracterizing God and being less supportive, Job started slipping, taking His eyes off of God and looking at his circumstances instead. Do you sometimes let others distract you from your focus? What does that look like for you? How can you stay strong, keep your eyes on God, and stay the course on this fitness journey even amongst the distractions?

_____

_____

_____

_____

Today's VICTORY

_____

_____

_____

Scripture Writing: Nehemiah 9:31

_____

_____

_____

_____

_____

Week 2 Day 3 | *Old Testament Heroes: Daniel*

Daily Spiritual Exercise: Meditate on an attribute of God.

Which attribute did you choose and why?

_____

_____

_____

_____

Daniel did not let fear of the lions distract him from worshiping and trusting God. What "lions" do you face daily? Junk food? Healthy food you don't like? Making time to sleep? Not working out? Working out too much? List your lions. How can you stop worrying about what they *might* do rather than what the Lord *can* do? Where are you placing your focus? From where are you drawing your strength? Your confidence?

_____

_____

_____

_____

Today's VICTORY

_____

_____

_____

_____

Scripture Writing: Psalm 144:2

_____

_____

_____

_____

Week 2 Day 4 | *Old Testament Heroes: Abraham*

Daily Spiritual Exercise: Meditate on an attribute of God.

Which attribute did you choose and why?

Abraham raised the knife to slay his son, but God provided a ram instead. You too should expect and trust that God will provide. But if He doesn't make your fitness easier, make you healthier, stronger or lighter, are you still prepared to "raise the knife"? Are you still willing to sacrifice things you love as an act of obedience to the One you love more? How will your fitness change if you are committed to make sacrifices regardless of the results you may see on this earth?

Today's VICTORY

Scripture Writing: Deuteronomy 7:9

REFLECT

How is your week going so far? Are you reading daily? How is the meditation going?

How is your nutrition this week? How about your exercise and sleep? Is there anything you need to put in place today that will help you for the remainder of this week?

"No discipline seems pleasant at the time, but painful. Later on, however, it produces a harvest of righteous-ness and peace for those who have been trained by it."
—Hebrews 12:11

Week 2 Day 5 | *Old Testament Heroes: Solomon*

Daily Spiritual Exercise: Meditate on an attribute of God.

Which attribute did you choose and why?

On page 50, we read that Solomon "asks for what he needs, not what he wants." What do you think about that?

Today's VICTORY

Scripture Writing: Psalm 89:8

Week 2 Day 6 | *Old Testament Heroes: The "Here I Ams"*

Daily Spiritual Exercise: Meditate on an attribute of God.

Which attribute did you choose and why?

_____

_____

_____

_____

Is there any area of your fitness (exercise/nutrition/sleep) where you are hesitant to say, "Here I Am"? What would change if you were fully available to God?

_____

_____

_____

_____

_____

Today's VICTORY

_____

_____

_____

_____

Scripture Writing: Deuteronomy 32:4

_____

_____

_____

_____

Week 2 Day 7 | *Old Testament Heroes: Manoah & His Wife*

Daily Spiritual Exercise: Meditate on an attribute of God.

What attribute did you choose and why?

_____

_____

_____

_____

Did you know who Manoah was before today? Do you believe that God wants to be God in all areas of your life, including your fitness?

_____

_____

_____

_____

_____

Today's VICTORY

_____

_____

_____

_____

Scripture Writing: Jeremiah 9:23–24

_____

_____

_____

_____

Weekly Recap

Use the space below to comment on anything that struck you as you were reading. Were you especially encouraged by something? Convicted? Confused? Motivated? The list could go on and on. Write down today's date and what God is revealing to you. Then, come back and read it in a year or two or 10 to see how God has interceded.

Week 3 Preview | *Names for God*

Do you find that you rely more on yourself than on God to get through your daily life? How will looking at the different names of God make a difference? Could understanding His character help you to start relying on the Holy Spirit, rather than yourself, to live a healthier lifestyle?

Week 3 Day 1 | *Names for God: The Potter*

Daily Spiritual Exercise: Sing a song of praise.

What song did you choose and why?

Page 61 says that "God has an ordained purpose specific to us." Isaiah 64:8 says God is the Potter who made you to be YOU, not anybody else! Do you compare yourself to others? If you stopped, how would your life change?

Today's VICTORY

Scripture Writing: Romans 9:21

Week 3 Day 2 | *Names for God: Breath of Life*

Daily Spiritual Exercise: Sing a song of praise.

What song did you choose and why?

_____

_____

_____

_____

Page 64 says, "Exercise is a privilege, not a sacrifice." Have you or someone you love ever experienced a time when you were sick or hurt and unable to be active? How does switching your mindset to being grateful for the opportunity and ability to exercise change your perspective?

_____

_____

_____

_____

Today's VICTORY

_____

_____

_____

_____

Scripture Writing: Genesis 2:7

_____

_____

_____

_____

Week 3 Day 3 | *Names for God: Father*

Daily Spiritual Exercise: Sing a song of praise.

What song did you choose and why?

The respect we have for God should manifest itself into our words and deeds, including respecting our body. Are you showing respect? If not, what needs to change? Write one thing that you can change today to begin showing more respect to your Father through your fitness.

Today's VICTORY

Scripture Writing: Job 19:25–27

Week 3 Day 4 | *Names for God: Dwelling Place*

Daily Spiritual Exercise: Sing a song of praise.

What song did you choose and why?

_____

_____

_____

_____

REFLECT

How is your week going so far? Are you reading daily? Singing songs of praise?

How is your nutrition this week? How about your exercise and sleep? Is there anything you need to put in place today that will help you for the remainder of this week?

"Plans fail for lack of counsel, but with many advisers they succeed."
—Proverbs 15:22

Are you willing to let God change you on the inside, emotionally and spiritually? List some of the times when you struggle. During these times, are you dwelling in Him and on Him? Identifying moments that trigger anxiety is the first step in reminding yourself to turn to Him for help. He is dwelling in your heart and can strengthen you.

_____

_____

_____

Today's VICTORY

_____

_____

_____

Scripture Writing: Isaiah 40:17

_____

_____

_____

_____

_____

Week 3 Day 5 | *Names for God: Redeemer*

Daily Spiritual Exercise: Sing a song of praise.

What song did you choose and why?

Have you ever started a fitness plan and felt like you failed? Write about it below. How exactly did you feel? What would it feel like to consider that a learning experience rather than a failure? Remember, God is your Redeemer. He doesn't see your past "failings" as absolute predictors of future results. How does knowing that your past doesn't determine your future help keep your hope alive?

Today's VICTORY

Scripture Writing: Exodus 33:14

Week 3 Day 6 | *Names for God: Lord of Hosts*

Daily Spiritual Exercise: Sing a song of praise.

What song did you choose and why?

_____

_____

_____

_____

_____

In your greatest moments of need, to whom or what do you turn? Friends? Money? Family? Entertainment? Food? Give it some thought and be honest with yourself.

_____

_____

_____

_____

_____

Today's VICTORY

_____

_____

_____

_____

Scripture Writing: Matthew 11:28–30

_____

_____

_____

_____

_____

Week 3 Day 7 | *Names for God: God of Rest*

Daily Spiritual Exercise: Sing a song of praise.

What song did you choose and why?

_____

_____

_____

> *Today you are 21 days into your journey. Pause and pat yourself on the back for reaching that milestone! Twenty-one days is a great start to lay the groundwork for a habit to start forming. So, be encouraged! No matter how small it has looked, these first three weeks are pivotal because they lay the foundation for the rest of your success.*

Do you get adequate sleep? Does identifying God as *the God of rest* help you to place importance on your nightly sleep?

_____

_____

_____

Today's VICTORY

_____

_____

_____

Scripture Writing: Isaiah 6:3

_____

_____

_____

Weekly Recap

Use the space below to comment on anything that struck you as you were reading. Were you especially encouraged by something? Convicted? Confused? Motivated? The list could go on and on. Write down today's date and what God is revealing to you. Then, come back and read it in a year or two or 10 to see how God has interceded.

Flame Phase

Congratulations! You've spent the last three weeks in the *Fire Phase*. You have laid a foundation of focusing on your faith to power your fitness. Well done!

You are now officially in the *Flame Phase*. That means you are still warm, but not nearly as hot as you were initially. Early results begin to taper and the realization that this is a lifestyle starts to set in. While you're still interested in the pursuit, the fire has certainly faded to a flame.

Take a moment and reflect. How are you feeling at this phase of the journey? Do you still remember your "Why"? Do you need to make any adjustments to your goals or your plan of action going forward? Write down your thoughts below.

Remember, God is for you. He is with you. He is in you… every step of the way!

"Let your eyes look straight ahead; fix your gaze directly before you."
—Proverbs 4:25

Week 4 Preview | *The King of "Un"*

Committing to living a healthy lifestyle can be overwhelming. Does it offer comfort to you to know that our powerful God is on your side? How does holding on to this truth change your confidence in your ability to fulfill this commitment?

_____

_____

_____

_____

_____

_____

_____

_____

_____

_____

_____

_____

_____

_____

_____

_____

_____

_____

_____

_____

_____

_____

Week 4 Day 1 | *The King of "Un": Undone*

Daily Spiritual Exercise: Memorize a favorite Scripture reflecting God's ability to *undo* our mess.

On page 9, you were asked to define success. What issues, if any, are keeping you from having success with your fitness? Food? Lack of motivation or energy or time or knowledge? Whatever is getting in the way, present it to the Lord and ask Him to help you conquer it and lead you to victory.

_____

_____

_____

_____

_____

_____

Today's VICTORY

_____

_____

_____

_____

_____

Scripture Writing: Write out the Scripture you have chosen for today's Daily Spiritual Exercise.

_____

_____

_____

_____

_____

Week 4 Day 2 | *The King of "Un": Unconventional*

Daily Spiritual Exercise: Memorize a favorite Scripture reflecting God's *unconventional* ways.

Page 87 says, "Given that God does things differently, have you considered that He has plans for your fitness struggles?" Share your thoughts on this statement:

_____

_____

_____

_____

_____

_____

_____

Today's VICTORY

_____

_____

_____

_____

_____

_____

Scripture Writing: Write out the Scripture you have chosen for today's Daily Spiritual Exercise.

_____

_____

_____

_____

_____

Week 4 Day 3 | *The King of "Un": Unfailing*

Daily Spiritual Exercise: Memorize a favorite Scripture reflecting God's *unfailing* love.

With God, nothing is wasted. It is encouraging to know that He can use all our past efforts for His glory. With this in mind, what have you learned from your past experiences?

_____
_____
_____
_____

Today's VICTORY

_____
_____
_____
_____
_____

Scripture Writing: Write out the Scripture you have chosen for today's Daily Spiritual Exercise.

_____
_____
_____
_____
_____

REFLECT

How is your week going so far? Are you reading daily? What about the scripture memorization?

How is your nutrition this week? How about your exercise and sleep? Is there anything you need to put in place today that will help you for the remainder of this week?

"May he give you the desire of your heart and make all your plans succeed."
—Psalm 20:4

Week 4 Day 4 | *The King of "Un": Unparalleled*

Daily Spiritual Exercise: Memorize a favorite Scripture reflecting the *unparalleled* faithfulness of God's character.

God is faithful. He is there when you are struggling and there when you are having success. Spend some time thanking Him for that faithfulness.

_____

_____

_____

_____

_____

_____

Today's VICTORY

_____

_____

_____

_____

_____

_____

_____

Scripture Writing: Write out the Scripture you have chosen for today's Daily Spiritual Exercise.

_____

_____

_____

_____

_____

Week 4 Day 5 | *The King of "Un": Unchanging*

Daily Spiritual Exercise: Memorize a favorite Scripture reflecting God's *unchanging* nature.

In today's reading, there are several Scriptures listed that represent a facet of God's character that is unchanging, such as: His intentions, His word, His strength, His faithfulness, His purposes, His promises, etc. Which one resonated with you the most? Why?

Today's VICTORY

Scripture Writing: Write out the Scripture you have chosen for today's Daily Spiritual Exercise.

Week 4 Day 6 | *The King of "Un": Unrelenting*

Daily Spiritual Exercise: Memorize a favorite Scripture demonstrating God's *unrelenting* love.

"Throughout Scripture, we have one example after another of good news: God demonstrating a love that met the physical, emotional, and spiritual needs of His children. I would bet that if you look at your life, you could find example after example of Him doing the same." – Page 99

What is a physical need (related to fitness) that God has met in your life? Give an example also of an emotional need He has met. Then list a few spiritual needs that God has met in your life.

_____

_____

_____

_____

_____

Today's VICTORY

_____

_____

_____

_____

_____

Scripture Writing: Write out the Scripture you have chosen for today's Daily Spiritual Exercise.

_____

_____

_____

_____

Week 4 Day 7 | *The King of "Un": Unending*

Daily Spiritual Exercise: Memorize a Scripture that portrays the *unending* nature of God's love, grace, glory and provision.

Ephesians 3:20 says, "Now to him who is able to do immeasurably more than all we ask or imagine, according to his power that is at work within us…." What stands out to you about this verse? How is it a game-changer for your fitness journey and for your life?

_____

_____

_____

_____

_____

Today's VICTORY

_____

_____

_____

_____

_____

Scripture Writing: Write out the Scripture you have chosen for today's Daily Spiritual Exercise.

_____

_____

_____

_____

_____

Weekly Recap

Use the space below to comment on anything that struck you as you were reading. Were you especially encouraged by something? Convicted? Confused? Motivated? The list could go on and on. Write down today's date and what God is revealing to you. Then, come back and read it in a year or two or 10 to see how God has interceded.

Week 5 Preview | *Names for the Holy Spirit*

How can the practice of spiritual breathing (exhaling the impure and inhaling the pure) help you continue this journey in healthy living? If you focus on releasing the negative and receiving His pure control and empowerment, how could it change your habit of going to the wrong sources for renewal and comfort?

Week 5 Day 1 | *Names for the Holy Spirit: Counselor*

Daily Spiritual Exercise: Practice "spiritual breathing" throughout the day.

Page 108 says, "If we want to benefit from the Counselor and if we want to glorify the Father, we must listen and we must follow His perfect counsel." Knowing isn't the hard part. Listening and obeying are harder. In what areas are you having trouble obeying His counsel?

_____

_____

_____

_____

_____

Today's VICTORY

_____

_____

_____

_____

_____

Scripture Writing: John 14:16–17; 26

_____

_____

_____

_____

_____

_____

_____

Week 5 Day 2 | *Names for the Holy Spirit: Spirit of Life*

Daily Spiritual Exercise: Practice "spiritual breathing" throughout the day.

Page 110 states, "With fitness, it's easier to focus on the sacrifices rather than the benefits." Do you fall victim to the mindset of dwelling on the sacrifices? If so, why do you think that is? How can you shift your mindset? If this isn't a struggle for you, how do you keep from thinking this way?

Today's VICTORY

Scripture Writing: Luke 11:13

Week 5 Day 3 | *Names for the Holy Spirit: Advocate*

Daily Spiritual Exercise: Practice "spiritual breathing" throughout the day.

The Holy Spirit is actively working to empower you and to bring glory back to God the Father. Do you believe the Holy Spirit can change your desires? Can you see a future where you desire and crave exercising, healthy food, getting more sleep or whatever you are striving for on this journey? Have you actually asked Him to help you make this change? Do you *really* believe God can empower you and bring glory back to Him? Why or why not?

Today's VICTORY

Scripture Writing: Acts 1:8

Week 5 Day 4 | *Names for the Holy Spirit: Seal*

Daily Spiritual Exercise: Practice "spiritual breathing" throughout the day.

Do you sometimes think you don't deserve good things? Does that kind of thinking honor God when you know you have been sealed by the Holy Spirit, and He lives in you?

_____

_____

_____

_____

Today's VICTORY

_____

_____

_____

_____

_____

_____

Scripture Writing: Ephesians 1:13–14

_____

_____

_____

_____

_____

REFLECT

How is your week going so far? Are you reading daily? Are you getting the hang of "spiritual breathing"?

How is your nutrition this week? How about your exercise and sleep? Is there anything you need to put in place today that will help you for the remainder of this week?

"Suppose one of you wants to build a tower. Won't you first sit down and estimate the cost to see if you have enough money to complete it?"
—Luke 14:28

Week 5 Day 5 | *Names for the Holy Spirit: Spirit of Wisdom*

Daily Spiritual Exercise: Practice "spiritual breathing" throughout the day.

Where do you find you need wisdom most in life? Why?

_____

_____

_____

_____

_____

_____

_____

Today's VICTORY

_____

_____

_____

_____

_____

_____

Scripture Writing: James 1:5–6

_____

_____

_____

_____

_____

_____

Week 5 Day 6 | *Names for the Holy Spirit: The Comforter*

Daily Spiritual Exercise: Practice "spiritual breathing" throughout the day.

Do you tend to reach for the wrong tools in your own form of spiritual or emotional DIY? How can you consistently remind yourself to be still and rely on the Holy Spirit within you?

_____

_____

_____

_____

_____

Today's VICTORY

_____

_____

_____

_____

_____

Scripture Writing: Titus 3:5–7

_____

_____

_____

_____

_____

_____

Week 5 Day 7 | *Names for the Holy Spirit: Spirit of Sonship*

Daily Spiritual Exercise: Practice "spiritual breathing" throughout the day.

Romans 8:12 reads, "Therefore, dear brothers and sisters, you have no obligation to do what your flesh urges you to do." Does this verse help you in your battles of "the flesh"?

_____

_____

_____

_____

Today's VICTORY

_____

_____

_____

_____

_____

_____

Scripture Writing: Romans 8:15

_____

_____

_____

_____

_____

_____

Weekly Recap

Use the space below to comment on anything that struck you as you were reading. Were you especially encouraged by something? Convicted? Confused? Motivated? The list could go on and on. Write down today's date and what God is revealing to you. Then, come back and read it in a year or two or 10 to see how God has interceded.

_____

_____

_____

_____

_____

_____

_____

_____

_____

_____

_____

_____

_____

_____

_____

_____

_____

Week 6 Preview | *The Full Armor of God*

Are there times that you take off *the full armor of God*? You should **always** have His armor on and expect that Satan is going to attack you. Do you think it will change your mindset and behaviors when you are on full alert and expecting these struggles?

_____

_____

_____

_____

_____

_____

_____

_____

_____

_____

_____

_____

_____

_____

_____

_____

_____

_____

Week 6 Day 1 | *The Full Armor of God: Flesh & Blood*

Daily Spiritual Exercise: Write 1 Peter 5:8 on a sticky note and put it somewhere you will see it often.

Satan uses anything and everything to keep you from seeking God first. Food, TV, computers and _____ are not inherently bad. The issue is reaching for such things when we are struggling, rather than seeking our Heavenly Father.

How can you make sure to seek God first? If you do seek Him first, do you think He can help you keep balanced? Do you think if He is at the center of your fitness, He will allow you to enjoy the things He intended for your pleasure, without a hint of guilt?

Today's VICTORY

Scripture Writing: 1 Peter 5:8

Week 6 Day 2 | *The Full Armor of God: The Belt of Truth*

Daily Spiritual Exercise: Write Ephesians 6:13–14a on a sticky note and put it somewhere you will see it often.

Do you ever have negative self-talk? Write down one thing you often say to yourself that is negative. Then, rewrite it when you are wearing *the belt of truth*. Practice this every time you find yourself in the cycle of negativity.

Today's VICTORY

Scripture Writing: Ephesians 6:13–14a

Week 6 Day 3 | *The Full Armor of God: Breastplate of Righteousness*

Daily Spiritual Exercise: Write Philippians 4:7 on a sticky note and put it somewhere you will see it often.

The breastplate protects the heart, intestines and major organs. In Jewish culture, the heart and intestines represented the mind, will, disposition, emotions and feelings. That is where Satan usually attacks. In which areas do you find you most need to be on guard? Why?

Today's VICTORY

Scripture Writing: Philippians 4:7

Week 6 Day 4 | *The Full Armor of God: Feet Fitted with the Readiness of the Gospel of Peace*

Daily Spiritual Exercise: Write 2 Corinthians 1:21 on a sticky note and put it somewhere you will see it often.

Do you struggle with doubt, fear or anxiety in life, or in your fitness journey? How does this change when you realize that by standing firm and having God as your source of strength, hope and faith, He will give you victory?

REFLECT

How is your week going so far? Are you reading daily? Are the sticky notes a good reminder for you?

How is your nutrition this week? How about your exercise and sleep? Is there anything you need to put in place today that will help you for the remainder of this week?

"In their hearts humans plan their course, but the Lord establishes their steps."
—Proverbs 16:9

Today's VICTORY

_____

_____

_____

_____

Scripture Writing: 2 Corinthians 1:21

_____

_____

_____

_____

_____

Week 6 Day 5 | *The Full Armor of God: Shield of Faith*

Daily Spiritual Exercise: Write Psalm 91:4 on a sticky note and put it somewhere you will see it often.

Page 141 says, "In order to stop an arrow, we first need to take up the shield." What are some practical ways that you can take up *the shield of faith*?

_____

_____

_____

_____

_____

Today's VICTORY

_____

_____

_____

_____

_____

Scripture Writing: Psalm 91:4

_____

_____

_____

_____

_____

Week 6 Day 6 | *The Full Armor of God: Helmet of Salvation*

Daily Spiritual Exercise: Write Isaiah 26:3 on a sticky note and put it somewhere you will see it often.

Which area is the biggest struggle for you: discouragement, doubt or pride? Why?

Today's VICTORY

Scripture Writing: Isaiah 26:3

Week 6 Day 7 | *The Full Armor of God: Sword of the Spirit*

Daily Spiritual Exercise: Write Hebrews 4:12a on a sticky note and put it somewhere you will see it often.

God's Word defends, disarms and protects. His Word, *the Sword of the Spirit*, will win every time, but we must be ready to wield it. Are you ready? Why or why not?

_____

_____

_____

_____

_____

Today's VICTORY

_____

_____

_____

_____

Scripture Writing: Hebrews 4:12a

_____

_____

_____

_____

_____

_____

Weekly Recap

Use the space below to comment on anything that struck you as you were reading. Were you especially encouraged by something? Convicted? Confused? Motivated? The list could go on and on. Write down today's date and what God is revealing to you. Then, come back and read it in a year or two or 10 to see how God has interceded.

Fizzle Phase

You are now in the *Fizzle Phase*. Your results may have plateaued, which drives you in the wrong direction emotionally. In addition, the novelty of newness is completely gone and the flame is now barely an ember. **This is the danger zone where most people fall off the wagon**. So, how do you avoid that?

Re-examine your why. When you first started, you had goals and resolve. Reflect on them. Pull out your Mission Statement and read it again. If you skipped that part, take some time and do it now. Make a resolution for the remainder of this life-changing adventure.

Most importantly, resolve to honor God first in all things, and to look to Him for your strength and ability to endure. If you are being too hard on yourself and are unhappy with where you are at this point, then stop right this moment. Pray Romans 8:1: "There is now no condemnation for those who are in Christ Jesus." That includes you, no exceptions and no disclaimers. **Believe that. Do not allow yourself to be defeated by your own condemnation!**

How are you feeling about your journey right now? How are you going to set yourself up to conquer the *Fizzle Phase*? Do you need to make any adjustments to your goals or your plan of action going forward?

"Set your mind on things above, not on earthly things."
—Colossians 3:2

_____

_____

_____

_____

_____

_____

_____

_____

_____

Week 7 Preview | *Freedom*

Write a "Just Because" card to God below.

Week 7 Day 1 | *Freedom: From Guilt*

Daily Spiritual Exercise: Read Psalm 119 for your 3–5 minutes of adoration prayer today.

Is guilt over something weighing you down? If it is, confess it now and accept His gift of guiltlessness. God cleanses completely. Do you feel that weight lifting from your heart as you pray?

Today's VICTORY

Scripture Writing: Psalm 119:45

Week 7 Day 2 | *Freedom: For*

Daily Spiritual Exercise: Read Psalm 34 for your 3–5 minutes of adoration prayer today.

Are you so focused on what you are sacrificing that you are not enjoying the rewards? Have you ever heard someone say, "Don't miss Heaven for the world" or "Don't miss life for the moment"? What does this mean to you now?

Today's VICTORY

Scripture Writing: Psalm 34:4

Week 7 Day 3 | *Freedom: From Performance*

Daily Spiritual Exercise: Reflect on Psalms 103–104 for your 3–5 minutes of adoration prayer today.

You can't earn God's love. He loves you just as you are. Read the Letter from God again. How do you feel knowing His love is not based on your performance?

_____

_____

_____

_____

_____

_____

Today's VICTORY

_____

_____

_____

_____

_____

Scripture Writing: Psalm 103:2–5

_____

_____

_____

_____

_____

_____

_____

Week 7 Day 4 | *Freedom: From Perfection*

Daily Spiritual Exercise: Reference Psalm 19 for your 3–5 minutes of adoration prayer today.

Page 161 says, "Perfection stems from and leads to pride, which, at its heart, is the inability or unwillingness to fully embrace His grace." Do you struggle with trying to be perfect? Does the quote from page 161 help relieve you of the need for perfection? Why or why not?

REFLECT

How is your week going so far? Are you reading daily? How are your adoration prayers going?

How is your nutrition this week? How about your exercise and sleep? Is there anything you need to put in place today that will help you for the remainder of this week?

"For I know the plans I have for you, declares the Lord, plans to prosper you and not to harm you, plans to give you hope and a future."
—Jeremiah 29:11

_____
_____
_____
_____
_____

Today's VICTORY

_____
_____
_____
_____
_____

Scripture Writing: Psalm 19:7

_____
_____
_____
_____
_____

Week 7 Day 5 | *Freedom: From Bondage*

Daily Spiritual Exercise: Use Psalm 18 for the foundation of your 3–5 minutes of adoration prayer today.

How are you like the bumblebee? What can you do to stand fast, stay out of the porch and fly free?

Today's VICTORY

Scripture Writing: Psalm 18:32

Week 7 Day 6 | *Freedom: From the Law of Sin*

Daily Spiritual Exercise: Read Romans 8:1–16 and use it to guide you through your 3–5 minutes of adoration prayer today.

Where do you most need to experience freedom in your life?

_____

_____

_____

_____

_____

_____

Today's VICTORY

_____

_____

_____

_____

_____

Scripture Writing: Romans 8:5

_____

_____

_____

_____

_____

_____

Week 7 Day 7 | *Freedom: From Our Old Identity*

Daily Spiritual Exercise: Reference Psalm 136 for your 3–5 minutes of adoration prayer today. After each verse, add to your prayer, "He has freed me from _____."

Page 172 says, "Too often, we let our past become our identity. We let our struggles define us." How have you fallen victim to this in your life? Can you identify areas where you've allowed your mistakes or failures to characterize you? Have you been able to overcome this tension between the "old you" and the "new you"? What are practical steps you can take to live as a new creation in Christ?

_____

_____

_____

_____

Today's VICTORY

_____

_____

_____

_____

Scripture Writing: Ephesians 4:22–24

_____

_____

_____

_____

_____

Weekly Recap

Use the space below to comment on anything that struck you as you were reading. Were you especially encouraged by something? Convicted? Confused? Motivated? The list could go on and on. Write down today's date and what God is revealing to you. Then, come back and read it in a year or two or 10 to see how God has interceded.

Fortitude Phase

Well done! You are hanging in there. It may be getting more difficult to keep your "head in the game" as you hit this stage. Slowly, you start dropping some of the good habits you were developing. You might be missing workouts, staying up later or letting bad nutrition ease back into your life. If so, let this be your wake-up call! Now is the time to dig deep. You must develop perseverance and fortitude!

Fortitude: a strength of mind, heart, and will, that enables a person to encounter danger or bear pain or adversity with courage.

In the *Fortitude Phase*, it is crucial to just keep going. If you stick with it, you should start seeing some new results emerging at the end of the two weeks. Physical changes, as well as spiritual and emotional changes, are coming.

So, how can you get that strength of mind to just keep going? What must you do to "stay in the game?" Look at your Mission Statement again. Do you need to make any adjustments to your goals or your plan of action going forward?

"But as for you, be strong and do not give up, for your work will be rewarded."
—2 Chronicles 15:7

Week 8 Preview | *Promises in the Bible*

Have you made promises to God that you have trouble keeping? What changes must you make in order to keep your promises?

_____

_____

_____

_____

_____

_____

_____

_____

_____

_____

_____

_____

_____

_____

_____

_____

_____

_____

_____

Week 8 Day 1 | *Promises in the Bible: Mercies*

Daily Spiritual Exercise: Meditate for 3–5 minutes on Lamentations 3:22–23.

God's mercies are new every morning! He can take the chaos that is our lives and make something wonderful out of it. Reflect on His mercies and spend a few minutes praising Him for this incredible gift.

Today's VICTORY

Scripture Writing: Lamentations 3:22–23

Week 8 Day 2 | *Promises in the Bible: Prayer*

Daily Spiritual Exercise: Meditate for 3–5 minutes on Philippians 4:6–7.

What spoke to you most in the reading about prayer? Do you struggle with prayer? Do you have faith that God hears and answers your prayers?

_____

_____

_____

_____

_____

Today's VICTORY

_____

_____

_____

_____

Scripture Writing: Philippians 4:6–7

_____

_____

_____

_____

_____

Week 8 Day 3 | *Promises in the Bible: Help in Our Weakness*

Daily Spiritual Exercise: Meditate for 3–5 minutes on Romans 8:26–27.

Page 184 says, "According to Romans, the Spirit searches our hearts and acts on our behalf. He takes our aching groans and makes our prayers presentable to our Father." Do you think you may be praying for the wrong things as it relates to your fitness? If so, what might the Spirit be presenting to our Father on your behalf? What does it mean to you that, in our weakness, the Holy Spirit works to empower us?

_____

_____

_____

_____

Today's VICTORY

_____

_____

_____

_____

_____

Scripture Writing: Romans 8:26–27

_____

_____

_____

_____

_____

REFLECT

How is your week going so far? Are you reading daily? What are you learning in your meditation time?

How is your nutrition this week? How about your exercise and sleep? Is there anything you need to put in place today that will help you for the remainder of this week?

"Let the morning bring me word of your unfailing love, for I put my trust in you. Show me the way I should go, for to you I entrust my life."
—Psalm 143:8

Week 8 Day 4 | *Promises in the Bible: All Things*

Daily Spiritual Exercise: Meditate for 3–5 minutes on the promises found in Romans 8:28.

Lift up those areas in your life that you need God to work for your good and His glory.

_____

_____

_____

_____

_____

Today's VICTORY

_____

_____

_____

_____

Scripture Writing: Romans 8:28

_____

_____

_____

_____

_____

Week 8 Day 5 | *Promises in the Bible: He'll Provide*

Daily Spiritual Exercise: Meditate for 3–5 minutes on Matthew 6:26.

The word "worry" actually comes from an Old English word that means "to strangle."
Doesn't strangle aptly describe how we feel when we worry? How do you handle worry?

_____

_____

_____

_____

_____

_____

Today's VICTORY

_____

_____

_____

_____

_____

Scripture Writing: Matthew 6:26

_____

_____

_____

_____

_____

_____

Week 8 Day 6 | *Promises in the Bible: Iron Sharpens Iron*

Daily Spiritual Exercise: Read the following verses from Proverbs: 12:26, 17:17, 18:24, 27:6, 27:9, and 27:17. After deciding which verse is your favorite, meditate on it for 3–5 minutes.

Did you take a look at your five closest friends? What did that look reveal? If you're still struggling with your fitness, do you need to reach out to a true friend for accountability?

Today's VICTORY

Scripture Writing: Pick your favorite from this list: Proverbs: 12:26, 17:17, 18:24, 27:6, 27:9, and 27:17.

Week 8 Day 7 | *Promises in the Bible: Desires of Your Heart*

Daily Spiritual Exercise: Read Psalm 37:1–7a.

Share your thoughts on the following text taken from page 197: "What if our hearts took a permanent posture of awe and wonder at what the Lord does? What if we trusted Him to take care of our desires for us? What do you think He would want to do for and with a heart so submitted and respectful?"

Today's VICTORY

Scripture Writing: Psalm 37:5–7a

Weekly Recap

Use the space below to comment on anything that struck you as you were reading. Were you especially encouraged by something? Convicted? Confused? Motivated? The list could go on and on. Write down today's date and what God is revealing to you. Then, come back and read it in a year or two or 10 to see how God has interceded.

Week 9 Preview | *Running the Race*

This week you are going to practice praying out loud as part of your Daily Spiritual Exercise. How do you think actually hearing your voice as you pray will be different than praying silently? Do you see how talking to God aloud can reinforce what you are attempting to say?

Week 9 Day 1 | *Running the Race: The Purpose*

Daily Spiritual Exercise: Read aloud Psalm 139.

Do you find yourself motivated by pride, guilt, influence or something other than honoring God? If God searched your heart and tested your thoughts, where would He point out that you needed new direction? Would you let Him reshape your inward focus into something upward focused and God glorifying?

_____

_____

_____

_____

Today's VICTORY

_____

_____

_____

_____

_____

Scripture Writing: Write down the verses from Psalm 139 that spoke to you most.

_____

_____

_____

_____

_____

_____

_____

_____

Week 9 Day 2 | *Running the Race: The Plan*

Daily Spiritual Exercise: Read aloud the first chapter of the Book of James.

Have you made adjustments to the plan you created in the "mission statement" exercise? If you haven't . . . why not? Does it help to know that it is inevitable and expected to need changes to your plan?

_____

_____

_____

_____

_____

Today's VICTORY

_____

_____

_____

_____

_____

Scripture Writing: Write down the verses from James 1 that spoke to you most.

_____

_____

_____

_____

_____

_____

_____

Week 9 Day 3 | *Running the Race: The People*

Daily Spiritual Exercise: Read aloud Psalm 119.

On this journey, have you found yourself doing things "for the people" and not for God? Has your underlying mindset been "I'll show them" or "I'm a big deal"? How can you make sure you aren't putting more value on what people think than on what matters to God?

_____

_____

_____

_____

_____

_____

Today's VICTORY

_____

_____

_____

_____

_____

_____

Scripture Writing: Write down the verses from Psalm 119 that spoke to you most.

_____

_____

_____

_____

_____

Week 9 Day 4 | *Running the Race: The Pace*

Daily Spiritual Exercise: Read aloud Hebrews 11–12:3.

Our pace is perseverance. Though our routes on this fitness journey are all different, our pace should be similar. To win this race, our decision must be to never quit!

Can you honor God and keep going no matter how your health does or does not improve?

_____

_____

_____

_____

Today's VICTORY

_____

_____

_____

_____

_____

Scripture Writing: Write down the verses from Hebrews 11–12:5 that spoke to you most.

_____

_____

_____

_____

_____

_____

REFLECT

How is your week going so far? Are you reading daily? Is praying out loud a different experience for you?

How is your nutrition this week? How about your exercise and sleep? Is there anything you need to put in place today that will help you for the remainder of this week?

"Many are the plans in a person's heart, but it is the Lord's purpose that prevails."
—Proverbs 19:21

Week 9 Day 5 | *Running the Race: "The Wall"*

Daily Spiritual Exercise: Read aloud Philippians 1.

Page 213 says, "Setbacks in fitness, like those in life, are inevitable. Your responses to them will determine how quickly you recover … hitting a wall is really an opportunity to grow deeper in Christ." Share a time when you have hit "the wall." How did you handle it?

_____

_____

_____

_____

_____

_____

Today's VICTORY

_____

_____

_____

_____

_____

Scripture Writing: Write down the verses from Philippians 1 that spoke to you most.

_____

_____

_____

_____

_____

_____

Week 9 Day 6 | *Running the Race: The Breaks*

Daily Spiritual Exercise: Read aloud Isaiah 40.

Page 216 states, "Finishing strong requires refueling often. There's no better rest break than one spent with the only One who can truly renew your strength." How do you refuel? Are you in the habit of a weekly, daily, or hourly "rest break"? Why or why not?

Today's VICTORY

Scripture Writing: Write down the verses from Isaiah 40 that spoke to you most.

Week 9 Day 7 | *Running the Race: The Finish*

Daily Spiritual Exercise: Read aloud 1 Corinthians 9:24–27.

What does finishing well look like for you?

Today's VICTORY

Scripture Writing: Write out 1 Corinthians 9:24–27.

Weekly Recap

Use the space below to comment on anything that struck you as you were reading. Were you especially encouraged by something? Convicted? Confused? Motivated? The list could go on and on. Write down today's date and what God is revealing to you. Then, come back and read it in a year or two or 10 to see how God has interceded.

Week 10 Preview | *The Lord Is* _____

This week's spiritual exercise will likely be the most challenging you'll experience during your fitness journey . . . and potentially the most rewarding. Why? Because recounting on paper how the Lord has provided, protected, loved, and lavished his blessings on you is always a powerful testimony to His goodness and grace.

Every day this week, take some time to expand on the attribute used to describe the Lord. Use the space under each day's entry to explain how that attribute of the Lord has empowered, comforted or sustained you. **Do not skip this. Take your time and savor His faithfulness.**

Week 10 Day 1 | *The Lord Is: My Banner*

Daily Spiritual Exercise: Write a devotional prayer of praise.

How is the Lord your banner? Explain how this attribute of the Lord has empowered, comforted, or sustained you.

_____

_____

_____

_____

_____

Today's VICTORY

_____

_____

_____

_____

_____

_____

Scripture Writing: Exodus 17:11, 14–16a

_____

_____

_____

_____

_____

_____

Week 10 Day 2 | *The Lord Is: Good*

Daily Spiritual Exercise: Write a devotional prayer of praise.

How has the Lord been good to you? Explain.

Today's VICTORY

Scripture Writing: Psalm 106:1

Week 10 Day 3 | *The Lord Is: Close*

Daily Spiritual Exercise: Write a devotional prayer of praise.

How is the Lord close to you? Explain.

Today's VICTORY

Scripture Writing: Psalm 34:17–18

Week 10 Day 4 | *The Lord Is: Trustworthy*

Daily Spiritual Exercise: Write a devotional prayer of praise.

How has the Lord been trustworthy in your life? Explain.

_____

_____

_____

_____

_____

_____

REFLECT

How is your week going so far? Are you reading daily? What are you learning about the Lord as you write about Him?

How is your nutrition this week? How about your exercise and sleep? Is there anything you need to put in place today that will help you for the remainder of this week?

"The Lord is trustworthy in all he promises and faithful in all he does."
—Psalm 145:13b

Today's VICTORY

_____

_____

_____

_____

_____

Scripture Writing: Psalm 145:13–16

_____

_____

_____

_____

_____

_____

Week 10 Day 5 | *The Lord Is: Faithful*

Daily Spiritual Exercise: Write a devotional prayer of praise.

How has the Lord been faithful to you? Explain.

Today's VICTORY

Scripture Writing: 1 Corinthians 10:13–14

Week 10 Day 6 | *The Lord Is: A Warrior*

Daily Spiritual Exercise: Write a devotional prayer of praise.

How is the Lord your warrior? Explain.

Today's VICTORY

Scripture Writing: Exodus 15:3

Week 10 Day 7 | *The Lord Is: My Refuge*

Daily Spiritual Exercise: Write a devotional prayer of praise.

How is the Lord your refuge? Explain.

_____

_____

_____

_____

_____

_____

Today's VICTORY

_____

_____

_____

_____

_____

_____

Scripture Writing: Psalm 59:16

_____

_____

_____

_____

_____

_____

Weekly Recap

Use the space below to comment on anything that struck you as you were reading. Were you especially encouraged by something? Convicted? Confused? Motivated? The list could go on and on. Write down today's date and what God is revealing to you. Then, come back and read it in a year or two or 10 to see how God has interceded.

Flare Phase

You are now in the *Flare Phase*. Your persistence is paying off and results are emerging. Way to go! Take a moment to reflect on your accomplishment and God's goodness. In the end, it will be His goodness that empowers you to finish strong.

How are you feeling about your journey right now? Are you getting into a routine, learning better nutrition or improving your sleep? Do you need to make any adjustments to your goals or your plan of action to reignite the fire and finish strong?

"Let us not become weary in doing good, for at the proper time we will reap a harvest if we do not give up."
—Galatians 6:9

Week 11 Preview | *New Testament Heroes*

Is fasting something you have been comfortable doing in the past? If so, you know what a valuable practice it is to increase your intimacy with the Lord.

If you haven't fasted, that's okay. This will be a great time to learn.

When you fast, the hunger you feel is a reminder to be praying for a fully-surrendered life. When your stomach starts grumbling, make sure to keep your focus on God, rather than your discomfort. If you can't fast from food for a medical reason, consider something else instead: your phone, TV, social media, etc.

Look at your week ahead and decide which meal/item/activity you will be fasting from each day. Also, write down what you're hoping to learn from this Daily Spiritual Exercise.

_____

_____

_____

_____

_____

_____

_____

_____

_____

_____

_____

_____

Week 11 Day 1 | *New Testament Heroes: Joseph*

Daily Spiritual Exercise: Fast and pray.

Of the many things that stand out when reading about Joseph, consistency is at the top of the list.

What about you? Are you *consistently* making godly choices each day? What habits have you created in the last 10 weeks that you will be able to continue, not only for the next three weeks, but every day after? If your improvements are only temporary, what do you need to change to make them permanent?

Today's VICTORY

Scripture Writing: Matthew 6:16–18

Week 11 Day 2 | *New Testament Heroes: The Centurion*

Daily Spiritual Exercise: Fast and pray.

Love, Humility, Faith.

To be more like the centurion, what areas of your life need more growth?

_____

_____

_____

_____

_____

_____

Today's VICTORY

_____

_____

_____

_____

_____

_____

Scripture Writing: Romans 10:17

_____

_____

_____

_____

_____

_____

_____

Week 11 Day 3 | *New Testament Heroes: The Widow*

Daily Spiritual Exercise: Fast and pray.

Have you known people with health issues who still find joy in their fitness, despite not seeing the results they'd like? Have you reflected on how you will feel if you don't get the physical results you wanted? Can you be like the widow and give all you have on this journey, regardless of the outcome?

Today's VICTORY

Scripture Writing: Psalm 51:10

Week 11 Day 4 | *New Testament Heroes: Zacchaeus*

Daily Spiritual Exercise: Fast and pray.

If we're grumbling and half-hearted in our efforts, we are not honoring God. Do you truly seek Jesus with determination? Are you striving to see Him, know Him and learn more about Him? Are you approaching Him daily, even hourly, asking Him to display His power in your life, including your fitness life? When you can do that, everything changes.

REFLECT

How is your week going so far? Are you reading daily? Is fasting increasing your prayer life?

How is your nutrition this week? How about your exercise and sleep? Is there anything you need to put in place today that will help you for the remainder of this week?

"All this also comes from the Lord Almighty, whose plan is wonderful, whose wisdom is magnificent."
—Isaiah 28:29

_____

_____

_____

_____

Today's VICTORY

_____

_____

_____

_____

_____

Scripture Writing: 1 Corinthians 15:58

_____

_____

_____

_____

_____

_____

_____

Week 11 Day 5 | *New Testament Heroes: The Sick Woman*

Daily Spiritual Exercise: Fast and pray.

How would you complete this sentence? If I just _____ ,

then _____ .

Are you reaching for Jesus first? Do you truly believe in His power to help you? Why or why not?

_____

_____

_____

_____

_____

_____

Today's VICTORY

_____

_____

_____

_____

_____

Scripture Writing: Mark 9:23–24

_____

_____

_____

_____

_____

Week 11 Day 6 | *New Testament Heroes: Mary*

Daily Spiritual Exercise: Fast and pray.

Mary displayed humility, ongoing gratitude and kept an intentional awareness of what God was doing. What was your biggest takeaway from the example of Mary?

_____

_____

_____

_____

_____

_____

Today's VICTORY

_____

_____

_____

_____

_____

_____

Scripture Writing: Mark 10:27

_____

_____

_____

_____

_____

_____

Week 11 Day 7 | *New Testament Heroes: Silas*

Daily Spiritual Exercise: Fast and pray.

Page 269 asks, "Are you content with how God is using you for His purposes?" He may have a plan for even your fitness, whether your fitness is going strong or not. Can you continue to be faithful and honor Him with your heart – praying and praising – regardless of the outcome?

Today's VICTORY

Scripture Writing: Psalm 100:4–5

Weekly Recap

Use the space below to comment on anything that struck you as you were reading. Were you especially encouraged by something? Convicted? Confused? Motivated? The list could go on and on. Write down today's date and what God is revealing to you. Then, come back and read it in a year or two or 10 to see how God has interceded.

_____

_____

_____

_____

_____

_____

_____

_____

_____

_____

_____

_____

_____

_____

_____

_____

_____

_____

_____

Fun Phase

You are now in the *Fun Phase*. You're learning that hard work works! You are in the last two weeks of this 13-week journey! Are you elated that you didn't give up? We sure hope so!

Are you at the point where you can see having fitness as a lifestyle is realistic for you? Why or why not?

Take a few minutes to write down some of the victories you have had. Go back and read over the daily victories you recorded throughout this journey. Document some of the habits you have formed that will be life-changing for you. LIFE CHANGING! Take this time to thank God for helping you make it this far. Praise Him for helping you. Write down what you have learned.

Week 12 Preview | *The Fruit of the Spirit*

Page 271 says, "In order for the Holy Spirit to produce fruit in us, we have to provide the right environment in our hearts." Are you providing fertile ground as described in the reading? If not, what needs to change?

_____

_____

_____

_____

_____

_____

_____

_____

_____

_____

_____

_____

_____

_____

_____

_____

_____

_____

_____

Week 12 Day 1 | *The Fruit of the Spirit: Self Control*

Daily Spiritual Exercise: Focus on the fruit of self-control.

Do you struggle with self-control or willpower? Are you working out of your own strength? We are not called to rely on ourselves, but to allow the Holy Spirit to produce the fruit of self-control. Share your thoughts on this quote from page 275: "The problem of lacking self-discipline is not usually an awareness issue, it's an obedience issue."

Today's VICTORY

Scripture Writing: Titus 2:11–14

Week 12 Day 2 | *The Fruit of the Spirit: Joy*

Daily Spiritual Exercise: Focus on the fruit of joy.

Page 278 claims, "Joy can be your response regardless of what's going on in your life." Have you experienced joy in what should be joyless situations in your life? Why or why not?

Today's VICTORY

Scripture Writing: Psalm 19:7–8

Week 12 Day 3 | *The Fruit of the Spirit: Faithfulness*

Daily Spiritual Exercise: Focus on the fruit of faithfulness.

2 Timothy 2:13 says, "If we are faithless, he remains faithful, for he cannot disown himself." How can the fruit of faithfulness produced by the Holy Spirit change the outcome on this fitness journey and your faith journey?

_____

_____

_____

_____

_____

Today's VICTORY

_____

_____

_____

_____

Scripture Writing: Psalm 86:11–12

_____

_____

_____

_____

_____

_____

_____

REFLECT

How is your week going so far? Are you reading daily? Are you focusing on the Fruits of the Spirit and is it helping?

How is your nutrition this week? How about your exercise and sleep? Is there anything you need to put in place today that will help you for the remainder of this week?

"As the heavens are higher than the earth, so are my ways higher than your ways and my thoughts than your thoughts."
—Isaiah 55:9

Week 12 Day 4 | *The Fruit of the Spirit: Patience*

Daily Spiritual Exercise: Focus on the fruit of patience.

Are you generally patient or impatient? Are you patient with others, but not yourself? The Lord has been patient with you. Who are you not to be patient with yourself?

_____

_____

_____

_____

_____

_____

Today's VICTORY

_____

_____

_____

_____

_____

Scripture Writing: Hebrews 12:1–3

_____

_____

_____

_____

_____

_____

Week 12 Day 5 | *The Fruit of the Spirit: Peace*

Daily Spiritual Exercise: Focus on the fruit of peace.

Do you get caught up in the emotional highs and lows of your fitness progress and/or in life in general? How can the peace produced by the Holy Spirit help you navigate life?

_____

_____

_____

_____

_____

Today's VICTORY

_____

_____

_____

_____

_____

_____

Scripture Writing: Philippians 4:6–7

_____

_____

_____

_____

_____

_____

_____

Week 12 Day 6 | *The Fruit of the Spirit: Gentleness*

Daily Spiritual Exercise: Focus on the fruit of gentleness.

Did your definition of gentleness expand after today's reading? How?

_____

_____

_____

_____

_____

_____

Today's VICTORY

_____

_____

_____

_____

_____

Scripture Writing: Colossians 3:12–14

_____

_____

_____

_____

_____

_____

_____

Week 12 Day 7 | *The Fruit of the Spirit: Goodness*

Daily Spiritual Exercise: Focus on the fruit of goodness.

God's goodness protects, provides, renews, rescues, saves, liberates, forgives, forgets, instructs and is abundant. His news, His name, His word, His will, His judgment, His laws, His disciplines, His gifts and His love are good. Which aspect(s) of God's goodness resonated the most with you? Share below.

Today's VICTORY

Scripture Writing: Ephesians 5:8–10

Weekly Recap

Use the space below to comment on anything that struck you as you were reading. Were you especially encouraged by something? Convicted? Confused? Motivated? The list could go on and on. Write down today's date and what God is revealing to you. Then, come back and read it in a year or two or 10 to see how God has interceded.

Week 13 Preview | *Names for You*

When you look in the mirror what do you see? Are you sure you see yourself as God sees you?

_____

_____

_____

_____

_____

_____

_____

_____

_____

_____

_____

_____

_____

_____

_____

_____

_____

_____

_____

Week 13 Day 1 | *Names for You: Conqueror*

Daily Spiritual Exercise: Write: "Because of Christ, I am more than a conqueror."

Now, write down the implications this has in your life. What will it enable you to accomplish? How will being more than a conqueror affect your struggles or equip you for victory? Pray that God will help you to see yourself the way He sees you.

Today's VICTORY

Scripture Writing: Romans 8:37

Week 13 Day 2 | *Names for You: Citizen*

Daily Spiritual Exercise: Write: "Because of Christ, I am a citizen of heaven."

Now, write down the implications this has in your life. What will it enable you to accomplish? How will being a citizen of heaven affect your struggles or equip you for victory? Pray that God will help you to see yourself the way He sees you.

Today's VICTORY

Scripture Writing: Ephesians 2:19–22

Week 13 Day 3 | *Names for You: Child*

Daily Spiritual Exercise: Write down: "Because of Christ, I am a child of God."

Now, write down the implications this has in your life. What will it enable you to accomplish? How will being a child of God affect your struggles or equip you for victory? Pray that God will help you to see yourself the way He sees you.

Today's VICTORY

Scripture Writing: Romans 8:15–17

Week 13 Day 4 | *Names for You: Wonderfully Made*

Daily Spiritual Exercise: Write down: "I am wonderfully made."

Now, write down the implications this has in your life. What will it enable you to accomplish? How will being wonderfully made affect your struggles or equip you for victory? Pray that God will help you to see yourself the way He sees you.

Today's VICTORY

Scripture Writing: Psalm 139:13–14

REFLECT

How is your week going so far? Are you reading daily? Do you feel closer to the Father as you begin to see you the way He sees you?

How is your nutrition this week? How about your exercise and sleep? Is there anything you need to put in place today that will help you for the remainder of this week?

*"Do not wear yourself out to get rich;
do not trust your own cleverness."
—Proverbs 23:4*

Week 13 Day 5 | *Names for You: Precious*

Daily Spiritual Exercise: Write down: "I am precious in the eyes of God."

Now, write down the implications this has in your life. Then, post it somewhere you will see it regularly. Every time you see it, ask the Lord to help you believe that you are precious to Him. Pray that God will help you to see yourself the way He does.

Today's VICTORY

Scripture Writing: Psalm 139:17–18 (NLT)

Week 13 Day 6 | *Names for You: Masterpiece*

Daily Spiritual Exercise: Write down: "Because of Christ Jesus, I am God's masterpiece."

Next now, write down the implications this has in your life. What will it enable you to accomplish? How will being God's masterpiece affect your struggles or equip you for victory? Pray that God will help you to see yourself the way He sees you.

Today's VICTORY

Scripture Writing: Ephesians 2:10 (NLT)

You Did It!

You completed 90 days. We hope that you have seen your relationship with the Lord deepen. We pray you have experienced Him empowering you, so that you can bring Him glory with your mind, heart, soul and strength.

Never, ever, EVER, forget: this is about progress, not perfection. Even if you have not yet seen the physical results you desired, be sure to take time to reflect on the progress you have made. If nothing changed for you externally – but you persevered and completed this devotional – then you have already experienced a **major victory** in your fitness journey!

Now it is time to talk about your next steps. This is a very important part of any fitness journey. Resist the temptation to treat the completion of this journey as a break. It's not. It was, perhaps, the most important leg of the journey. This is the portion of the journey where you set your bearings and found that the Holy Spirit is now your endless, tireless and relentless well of energy, encouragement, and empowerment.

So, make a plan. Look at your Mission Statement from the beginning of the study and set new goals in the area of exercise, nutrition and sleep.

In the space below, take some time to write down your plans and any last thoughts. What have you learned on our journey together? What will you do differently from here on out? What victories has He accomplished on your behalf? How are things better for you now? What areas could still stand some improvement? How can you help others in this area? Have you considered leading a group through this study? Perhaps you could start a walking club? Or an online accountability group?

Chances are you have learned a lot. Share that below and make a plan to keep the momentum going.

_____

_____

_____

_____

_____

"I praise you because I am fearfully and wonderfully made; your works are wonderful, I know that full well."

—Psalm 139:14

NEXT STEPS

Thank you for taking this journey! We trust your faith deepened as you experienced the Lord empowering you to bring Him glory with your mind, body and spirit.

Remember, fitness is about progress, not perfection. Perhaps, you have not yet seen all the results you desire. Be sure to reflect on the progress you *have* made. If you persevered and completed the 13-week study, that is a major victory! You will see more victories, if you continue.

Now, it is time to talk about *next steps*. This is a critical point in the process. Many times, when we have gone through 90 days of effort, we want a break. That break can either be rejuvenating or it can be a slippery slope. We are here to help!

Here are some suggestions for your *next steps*.

1. Join a Challenge Group. You will find groups on BodyTithe.com. You can join others going through a specific workout program, nutrition challenge, sleep experiments, and more.

2. Do a couch-to-5k program. These can be excellent for beginners interested in training. You just need a road and some shoes. Find a partner for some increased accountability and you'll be on your way. Visit BodyTithe.com/couch-to-5k for more information.

3. If you struggled to give the study your full attention, go through the *Body Tithe Devotional Study Guide* again. Sometimes it takes an extra try or two before something really takes root. BodyTithe.com has groups for those going through the study.

4. Visit BodyTithe.com for more resources, including articles on exercise, nutrition, and sleep. We all need encouragement. We will point you back to the Father and what you have learned about how the Holy Spirit can empower your fitness regimen.

5. Use the included "Leader Guide" to lead a *Body Tithe Devotional* study group in your town. Big or small, it doesn't matter. Post something on social media. Call a few friends. You might be surprised at the response you get.

   The meetings don't need to be fancy. Just pick a time and a place (coffee shop, home, church, YMCA, library, etc.) where you can meet and get going.

You don't have to be perfect to lead a group. Too often, we think we don't have much to offer. All we really need is to be available and a little vulnerable.

6. Always remember: Hebrews 12:1–3. Run the race. Persevere. Don't give up. *Whatever you do, don't give up.* With Christ in you, supplying all that you need, we are confident you won't.

WE HAVE SOME FAVORS TO ASK

We hope you have been blessed by going through this study. Our prayer has been that you come to a greater understanding of both God's love for you and His power in you.

Would you consider taking a moment to write a *Body Tithe Devotional Study Guide* **review and post it on Amazon?** Reviews can be the lifeblood for books. The more encouragement to potential readers, the better. Or visit BodyTithe.com and send us the review. We really appreciate your reviews.

Also, **please share any feedback you may have on how to make the** *Study Guide* **more effective**. God is expanding the reach of BodyTithe.com and we want the study groups as applicable and encouraging as possible. You can send the feedback to info@bodytithe.com.

"May the God of hope fill you with all joy and peace as you trust in Him, so that you may overflow with hope by the power of the Holy Spirit."
—Romans 15:13

Finally, would you consider sharing about our ministry with your church? **This study is an easy way for your church to address the complicated issue of God-honoring body stewardship**. Nothing beats a personal testimony. Telling your pastors how *The Body Tithe Devotional Study* has worked in your life could open the door for more study groups in your town, helping others experience the freedom of faith-powered fitness.

Thank you again for taking this journey.

In Him,

Matthew, Kim, and Lorie

BODY TITHE DEVOTIONAL

LEADER GUIDE

HOW TO START A GROUP

- **Pray.** It is important to stop and pray before you take action. Ask for God's discernment concerning where to meet, what day and time of the week, who could join you in leading, who you should invite, and whether or not this is what He wants you to be doing right now. Ask others to pray with you and for you.

- **Find a time, date, and place to meet.** It is helpful to have these logistics worked out before you invite individuals. That said, let the Spirit lead you and don't worry about everything being perfect. The goal is to have individuals gather together to study His word and learn what He has to say about honoring Him in the area of body stewardship. A willing heart and flexibility are all that is really needed. Allow 60–90 minutes for each meeting.

- **Invite.** You can do this in person, via email/text, via social media, announcing it at your church, etc. Encourage those you invite to extend the invitation to friends.

- **Communicate.** Prior to the first meeting, send an informational email to the attendees, introducing the leaders, and reminding everyone the date, time, and location of the study group. Remind them also to have their copies of *The Body Tithe Devotional* and *The Body Tithe Devotional Study Guide* in preparation for the first meeting.

- **Pray some more.** Once you have your group formed, take time before your first meeting to pray for each individual participant. Ask God to do a mighty work in their lives through this study.

TIPS FOR LEADING A GROUP

- **NOTE:** This leader's guide is structured for a 14 week study with weekly meetings; however, we have also found it helpful to break the study down into two separate 7 week sessions and take a break in between. For example, you could start the study in mid-September and complete Sessions 1–7. Then, take a break for the holidays and start back mid-January with Sessions 8–14.

- **Pray.** We have prayer built into the opening and closing portions of your weekly meetings, but we also encourage you to prayerfully prepare for each group session by praying for each person in your group and asking the Holy Spirit to lead and guide you and your group.

- **Be inclusive.** Your goal is to foster community and make each person feel welcome. Always be intentional to invite new people to join your group, acknowledge visitors, and reconnect with anyone that misses a session, but then returns.

- **Be encouraging.** Your goal is to create a safe, uplifting environment for individuals to learn and be known. Participants will get out what they put into the study. So encourage them to do their assignments. That said, make sure they know it is okay to attend if they haven't. They are entering a no-judgment zone. The important thing is to meet each participant right where they are. Tell them that you know God is working in each person's life and they are loved, valued, and welcomed in the group.

- **Promote discussion.** Be sure to encourage conversation and participation, but politely redirect discussion if anyone dominates the conversation. Don't be afraid of silence. Often people need time to process their responses or build the courage to share. Be careful that you don't rush through questions. Allow plenty of time for sharing. Be engaged and listen to the answers given. There is no "right" answer, so be sure to give individuals space to share and be heard. Remember too that you don't have to get through all the questions we suggest for discussion. These are guidelines. If the Spirit is moving in a different direction in your group, then follow His lead.

- **Encourage connections.** Find ways to connect with individuals between group sessions. You can write notes or emails, send an encouraging text, make a phone call, encourage prayer/accountability partners, workout together as a group, or suggest that everyone trains to either run/walk a local 5K.

SESSION 1
INTRODUCTION

- **Pray.**

- **Welcome.** Introduce the study, yourself, and if applicable, the co-leader. If you feel comfortable, consider sharing your personal testimony and why you decided to start this study group.

- **Discuss.** Ask individuals to introduce themselves and share what drew them to the study. What are their expectations? Depending on the size of the group you can do this collectively as a group or circle up into smaller groups.

- Walk through How to Use this Study Guide (pages 6–7) with the group and use Week 1 Preview and Week 1 Day 1 (pages 10–11) as an example. Explain the importance of the daily habits of the Daily Spiritual Exercise (DSE), recording Today's Victory, and doing the Scripture Writing. Encourage them that if life happens and they can't get to the daily reading or answer the discussion question in the *Study Guide* to at least review the DSE, record a victory, and write the Scripture listed. Encourage them to focus on spending time renewing their mind and being still before the Lord and listening to His voice.

- **Take Action.** Set aside 10–15 minutes to have individuals spend time quietly reading over, praying about, and completing the Mission Statement exercise. (Pages 7–9)

- **Encourage.** Let everyone know that you believe in them. Remind them that Christ in them can bring victory and freedom to their lives. Encourage vulnerability. And tell them that the main focus is on spiritual fitness. If hearts can be transformed, the physical will follow.

- **Q&A Time**

- **Close with Prayer**

SESSION 2
WEEK 1 – Names for Jesus

- **Pray**

- **DSE & Victory Review**

  - Ask how the first week of study went and feedback on the first DSE of praying without ceasing.

  - Ask for individuals to share a victory they recorded.

- **Discuss**

  - Which name for Jesus was your favorite? Why?

  - Discuss the difference between being an inspiration and being a reflection. (Day 3)

  - What does it mean to you to "put down the pen"? (Day 6)

  - "Weekly Recap" page – have individuals share what they wrote in this section or suggest that they record their biggest takeaway from the week or today's group time.

- **DSE Preview – Meditate on an Attribute of God**

  - Discuss what this might look like, how to go about it, and give any tips you have on making it an effective exercise.

- **Close with Prayer**

SESSION 3
WEEK 2 – Old Testament Heroes

- **Pray**

- **DSE & Victory Review**

  - Ask for feedback on the DSE of meditating on an attribute of God. What was your favorite attribute? Why? Did you learn a new attribute?

  - Ask individuals to share a victory they recorded.

- **Discuss**

  - Who was your favorite Old Testament Hero? Why?

  - David was intentional in selecting his 5 stones. In what area(s) of your life do you need to be intentional? (Day 1)

  - What lions do you face? (Day 3)

  - Are you willing to sacrifice things you love as an act of obedience to the One you love more? How could your fitness change if you committed to make sacrifices regardless of the results you may see on this earth? (Day 4)

  - Did you know who Manoah was before today? Do you believe God wants to be God in all areas of your life, including your fitness? (Day 7)

  - "Weekly Recap" page – have individuals share what they wrote in this section or suggest that they record their biggest takeaway from the week or today's group time.

- **DSE Preview – Sing a Song of Praise**

  - Discuss what this might look like, how to go about it, and give any tips you have on making it an effective exercise.

- **Close with Prayer**

  - Pray this blessing over the group: "May you know how wide and long and high and deep is the love of Christ. May you be filled to the measure of all the fullness of God. May you not become weary in doing good, but rest in the fact that at the proper time you will reap a harvest if you do not give up. May you always know that you are worthy of love and belonging because who you are in Him is enough. You are more than a conqueror. What you do matters and has value. May you always know that regardless of what anyone says or thinks, God says you matter to Him."

SESSION 4
WEEK 3 – Names for God

• **Pray**

• **DSE & Victory Review**

  ◆ Ask individuals to share a song that they sang during the DSE last week.

  ◆ Ask individuals to share a victory they recorded.

• **Discuss**

  ◆ What was your favorite name for God? Why?

  ◆ Do you compare yourself to others? Why? How would your life change if you stopped? (Day 1)

  ◆ Are you showing yourself respect? If not, what needs to change? (Day 3)

  ◆ What makes you feel anxious? Do you turn to Him for help? (Day 4)

  ◆ Have you ever started something and felt like you failed? How would things change if you viewed this as a learning experience instead of a failure? (Day 5)

  ◆ "Weekly Recap" page – have individuals share what they wrote in this section or suggest that they record their biggest takeaway from the week or today's group time.

• **DSE Preview – Memorize a Scripture Passage**

  ◆ Discuss what this might look like, how to go about it, and give any tips you have on making it an effective exercise. NOTE: The book suggests memorizing a different Scripture each day, but some individuals are intimidated by Scripture memorization. Let them know if they want to memorize one passage for the entire week, that is perfectly fine.

• **Close with Prayer**

  ◆ **SUGGESTION:** Encourage individuals to pray about approaching someone to be an accountability/prayer/workout partner; maybe even someone in this study.

  ◆ Close with a song of praise as the prayer. You can pick one that has been especially meaningful to you for this journey. Here are a few other suggestions: "Great Are You Lord" by All Sons & Daughters, "So Will I (100 Billion X)" by Hillsong United, and "Living Hope" by Phil Wickham.

SESSION 5
WEEK 4 – The King of "Un"

• **Pray**

• **DSE & Victory Review**

  ◆ Ask individuals to share a Scripture they memorized.

  ◆ Ask individuals to share a victory they recorded.

• **Discuss**

  ◆ You are now fully entrenched in the "Flame Phase" of this journey. How are you feeling? (Page 37)

  ◆ Which "Un" connected with you? Why?

  ◆ Have you ever considered that God has plans for your struggles? (Day 2)

  ◆ Do you believe that with God nothing is wasted? Why or why not? (Day 3)

  ◆ Have someone read Ephesians 3:20 from their Bible. What stands out to you about this verse? (Day 7)

• **DSE Preview – Spiritual Breathing**

  ◆ Discuss what this is, how to go about it, and give any tips you have on making it an effective exercise.

• **Close with Prayer**

SESSION 6
WEEK 5 – Names for the Holy Spirit

- **Pray**

- **DSE & Victory Review**

  - Ask individuals about their experience with spiritual breathing.

  - Ask individuals to share a victory they recorded.

- **Discuss**

  - Which name for the Holy Spirit connected with you? Why?

  - In what areas are you having trouble listening and/or obeying? (Day 1)

  - Do you fall victim to the mindset of dwelling on the sacrifices? If so, why? (Day 2)

  - How can you consistently remind yourself to be still and rely on the Holy Spirit within you? (Day 6)

  - "Weekly Recap" page – have individuals share what they wrote in this section or suggest that they record their biggest takeaway from the week or today's group time.

- **DSE Preview – Sticky Note Scriptures**

  - Discuss what this might look like, how to go about it, and give any tips you have on making it an effective exercise. You may want to hand out fun sticky note pads to each participant to encourage them in doing the DSE.

- **Close with Prayer**

  - Have individuals pair up and pray for one another.

SESSION 7
WEEK 6 – The Full Armor of God

- **Pray**

- **DSE & Victory Review**

  - Ask individuals to share where they posted their sticky note Scriptures.

  - Ask individuals to share a victory they recorded.

- **Discuss**

  - Which piece of armor are you most drawn to? Why?

  - Do you ever have negative self-talk? If you do, what word did you write down? What word did you replace it with? (Day 2)

  - In what areas do you find you most need to be on guard from Satan's attacks? (Day 3)

  - What area is the biggest struggle for you: discouragement, doubt, or pride? Why? (Day 6)

  - Discuss the "Fizzle Phase" so as to be proactive against coming obstacles. (Page 65)

  - NOTE: If you are getting ready to take a break before starting the next 7 weeks of the study, encourage individuals to be prayerful during the break. The break in combination with the "Fizzle Phase" can be a stumbling block. Urge, implore, and plead with them to stay strong. They'll be glad they did when they reconvene.

- **DSE Preview – Adoration Prayer**

  - Discuss what this might look like, how to go about it, and give any tips you have on making it an effective exercise.

- **Close with Prayer**

SESSION 8
WEEK 7 – Freedom

- **Pray**

- **DSE & Victory Review**

  - Ask individuals to share which Scripture they enjoyed the most for their time of adoration prayer.

  - Ask individuals to share a victory they recorded.

  - If there was a break, ask how they did during the break, what they noticed, and what they learned.

- **Discuss**

  - Which day on freedom resonated the most with you? Why?

  - Are you so focused on what you are sacrificing that you are not enjoying the rewards? (Day 2)

  - How do you feel knowing His love is not based on your performance and you can't earn it? (Day 3)

  - Do you struggle with trying to be perfect? (Day 4)

  - How are you like the bumblebee? (Day 5)

  - "Weekly Recap" page – have individuals share what they wrote in this section or suggest that they record their biggest takeaway from the week or today's group time.

- **DSE Preview – Scripture Meditation**

  - Discuss what this might look like, how to go about it, and give any tips you have on making it an effective exercise.

- **Close with Prayer**

  - Read aloud together the "Dear Child" letter on page 158 and then have someone close in prayer thanking God that we are His children.

SESSION 9
WEEK 8 – Promises in the Bible

- **Pray**

- **DSE & Victory Review**

  - Ask individuals to share their experience with meditating on Scripture.

  - Ask individuals to share a victory they recorded.

- **Discuss**

  - What was your favorite promise?

  - What spoke to you most in the reading about prayer? Do you struggle with prayer? Do you have faith that God hears and answers your prayers? (Day 2)

  - What do you need God to work for your good and for His glory? (Day 4)

  - Discuss the meaning of the word worry. How do you handle worry? (Day 5)

  - Did you look at your five closest friends? What did you discover? (Day 6)

  - "Weekly Recap" page – have individuals share what they wrote in this section or suggest that they record their biggest takeaway from the week or today's group time.

  - Discuss the "Fortitude Phase."

- **DSE Preview – Read Scripture Out Loud**

  - Discuss what this might look like, how to go about it, and give any tips you have on making it an effective exercise.

- **Close with Prayer**

SESSION 10
WEEK 9 – Running the Race

- **Pray**

- **DSE & Victory Review**

  - Ask individuals to share their experience with reading Scripture out loud.

  - Ask individuals to share a victory they recorded.

- **Discuss**

  - What was your favorite part of running the race – the purpose, plan, people, "the wall", the pace, the breaks, or the finish?

  - If God searched your heart and tested your thoughts, where would He point out that you need new direction? (Day 1)

  - How can you make sure you aren't putting more value on what people think that on what matters to God? (Day 3)

  - Share a time when you hit "the wall". How did you handle it? (Day 5)

  - How do you refuel? (Day 6)

  - "Weekly Recap" page – have individuals share what they wrote in this section or suggest that they record their biggest takeaway from the week or today's group time.

- **DSE Preview – Write a Devotion**

  - Encourage individuals to not be overwhelmed by this activity, but DO NOT skip it. Just give it a good effort. Suggest that they look up the word given to describe the Lord and do a word study in Scripture or simply look up the definition (i.e. banner) in the dictionary and start writing about that. Remind them that there is no right or wrong. This is not about perfection. It's about journaling your thoughts about the Lord.

- **Close with Prayer**

- Select a Scripture to read out loud together (i.e. Psalm 139:23–24) and ask someone to close in prayer.

SESSION 11
WEEK 10 – The Lord is _____

- **Pray**

- **DSE & Victory Review**

  - Ask individuals to share their experience with writing a devotional.

  - Ask individuals to share a victory they recorded.

- **Discuss**

  - What was your favorite adjective for the Lord this week – my banner, good, close, trustworthy, faithful, warrior, or my refuge?

  - How would you define the word good? How has the Lord been good to you? (Day 2)

  - Do you struggle to view the Lord as trustworthy? (Day 4)

  - Do you have an easy/hard time viewing the Lord as a warrior? (Day 6)

- **DSE Preview – Fasting**

  - Share that the goal of fasting is to be in constant prayer/communion with our Father. As we desire the thing we are fasting from, we go to Him in prayer instead. In the book, Matthew mentions fasting one meal/day. But we also want to encourage you that fasting doesn't have to be just related to food. In fact, some might be better served by fasting from something else: Netflix, social media, technology (your phone, certain apps, games), TV, etc. Basically, anything that you don't want to give up or would struggle to fast from is a good thing to consider fasting from this week. Just give it a shot and see what God reveals to you.

- **Close with Prayer**

SESSION 12
WEEK 11 — New Testament Heroes

- **Pray**

- **DSE & Victory Review**

  - Ask individuals to share their experience with fasting.

  - Ask individuals to share a victory they recorded.

- **Discuss**

  - Who was your favorite New Testament hero from this week's reading? Why?

  - The centurion was characterized by love, humility, and faith? In which of these areas do you need to experience growth? (Day 2)

  - Do you seek Jesus with determination like Zacchaeus did? Why or why not? (Day 4)

  - What is your biggest takeaway from the example of Mary? (Day 6)

  - Are you content with how God is using you? (Day 7)

  - "Weekly Recap" page – have individuals share what they wrote in this section or suggest that they record their biggest takeaway from the week or today's group time.

  - You are now in what is known as the "Flare Phase." How are you feeling about this phase of your journey? (See page 103)

- **DSE Preview – Focus on a Fruit of the Spirit**

  - Suggest that they look up the definition of each fruit and even do a word study based on the original Greek to help them better understand each fruit

- **Close with Prayer**

SESSION 13
WEEK 12 — The Fruit of the Spirit

- **Pray**

- **DSE & Victory Review**

  - Ask individuals to share how they focused on a fruit of the Spirit.

  - Ask individuals to share a victory they recorded.

- **Discuss**

  - Which fruit resonated with you the most? Why?

  - Day 2 says, "Joy can be your response regardless of what's going on in your life." What are your thoughts about this quote?

  - Are you generally patient or impatient? Are you patient with others, but not yourself? How could being patient with yourself improve your life? (Day 4)

  - Did your definition of gentleness expand after today's reading? If so, how? (Day 6)

  - "Fun Phase" (see page 113). Ask individuals to share with the group what they are experiencing at this phase of their journey.

- **DSE Preview – Write Down His Names for You**

  - Discuss what this might look like, how to go about it, and give any tips you have on making it an effective exercise.

- **Close with Prayer**

SESSION 14
WEEK 13 – Names for You

- **Pray**

- **DSE & Victory Review**

  - Ask individuals to share their experience with writing down His names for you. Ask if they did this DSE. Why or why not?

  - Ask individuals to share a victory they recorded.

- **Discuss**

  - What name resonated most with you?

  - What are the life implications of being a citizen of heaven? What will it enable you to accomplish? (Day 2)

  - What does it mean to you to be fearfully and wonderfully made? Do you believe this about yourself? Why or why not? (Day 4)

  - What does being God's masterpiece mean to you? How does it affect your struggles or equip you for victory? (Day 6)

  - "Weekly Recap" page – have individuals discuss their next steps and share their plan of action if they wrote one down (see page 130).

  - Take some time to discuss pages 132–134. We have included some next step options for them to consider. Remind them that this study is laying the foundation for their continued body stewardship. If they are not intentional, they'll get distracted and their fitness will fall to the wayside.

  - Finally, would you please consider encouraging them to write a review on Amazon? It would mean a great deal to us and the future of this ministry.

- **Close with Prayer**

- Have everyone stand up and out loud read together "Because of Christ and in Christ" (page 320) and close with the prayer on Page 321 in the book.

Made in United States
North Haven, CT
28 December 2023

46712523R00083